Look What I Can Read!

Story by Anne W. Phillips
Illustrations by Darrin Johnston

HARCOURT BRACE & COMPANY

Orlando Atlanta Austin Boston San Francisco Chicago Dallas New York
Toronto London

I can read a story at school.

I can read a magazine outside.

I can read Grandma's letter.

I can read the comics with Dad.

I can read the directions.

I can read a book at home.

Anywhere, anytime, anything—
I can read what I like—
and that's everything!